Welcom e

MAD
MARKET

We've got...

Cucumbers!

Shoecumbers!

Goocumbers!

Moocumbers!

Newcumbers!

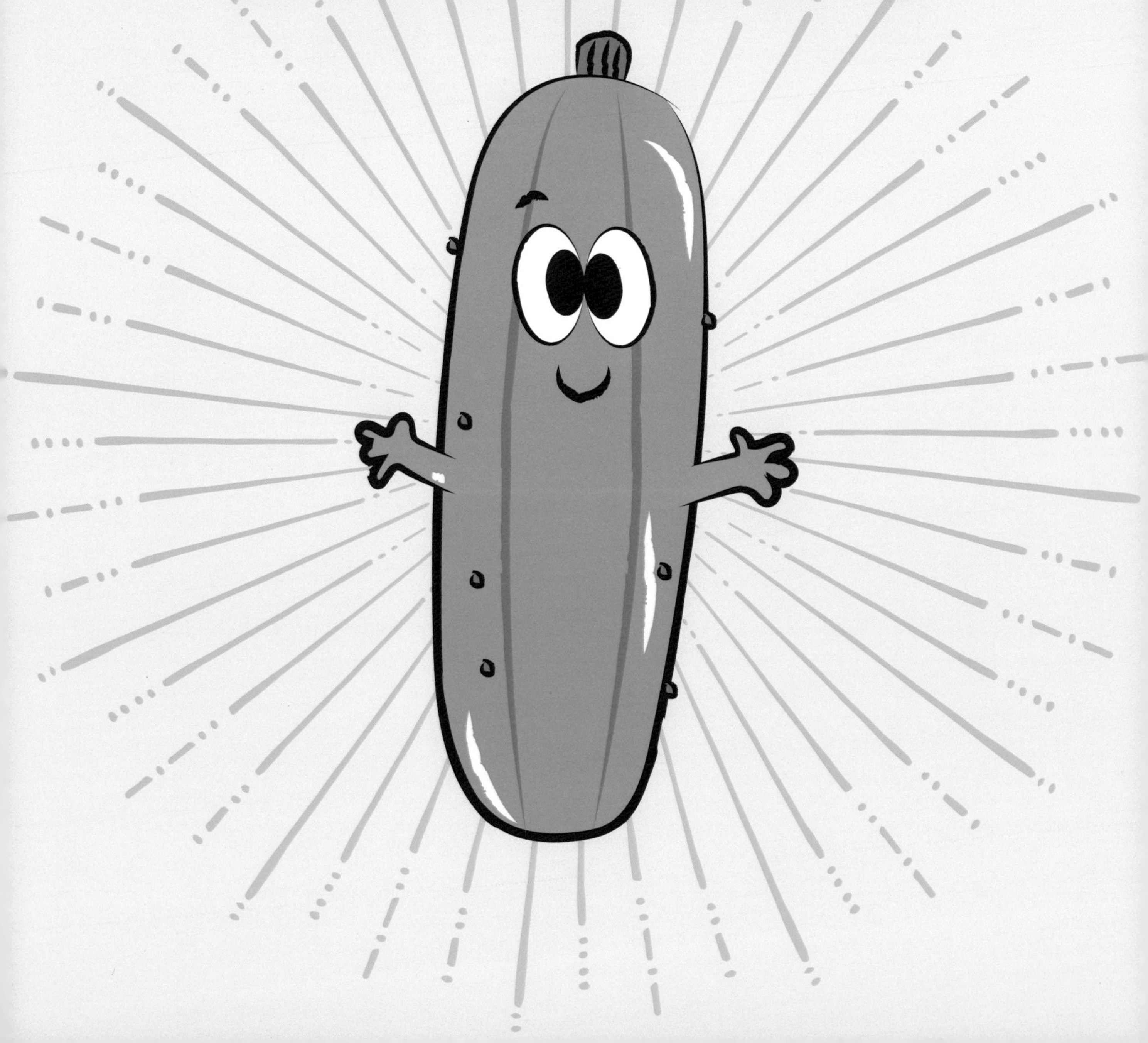

We're even stocking...

Poocumbers!

Bluecumbers!

Whocumbers!

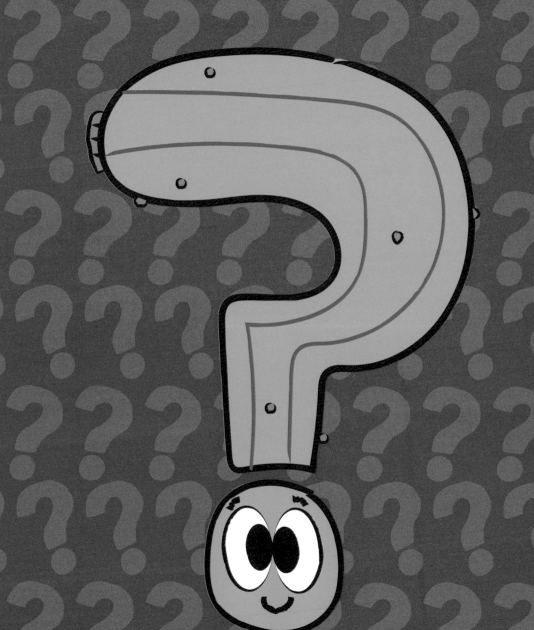

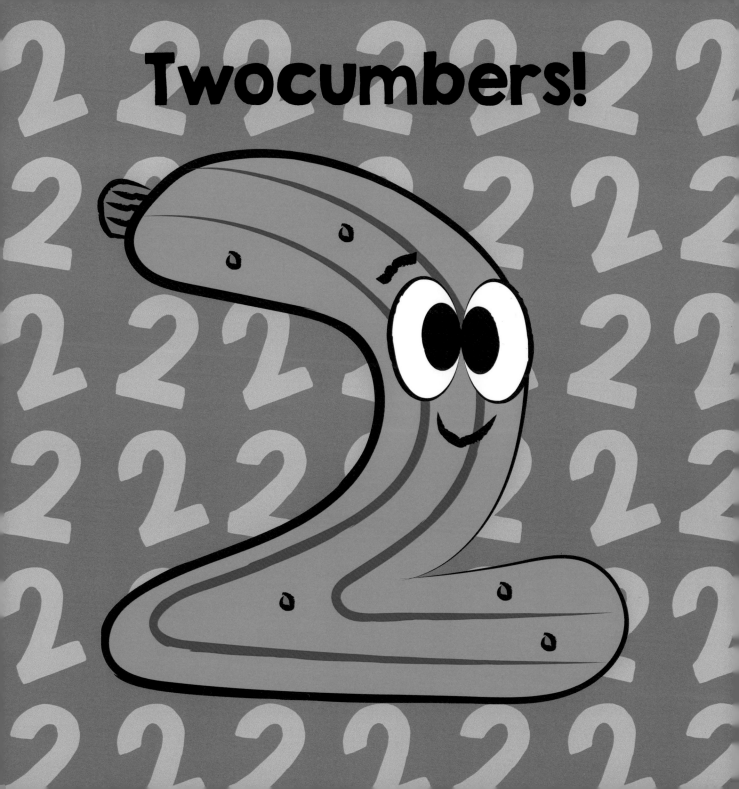

Gluecumbers!

Screwcumbers!

Zoocumbers!

All fresh today!

NOW YOU!

Now is your chance to create your own rhymes and poems using some ideas from the book.

You can even learn how to draw a cucumber!

Rhyme Time!

Circle all the words that rhyme with glue.

foot

cow

shoe

chew

flew

new

market

poo

zoo

blue

monkey

Shopping List

What words can you think of that rhyme with cucumber? Write them on your shopping list below!

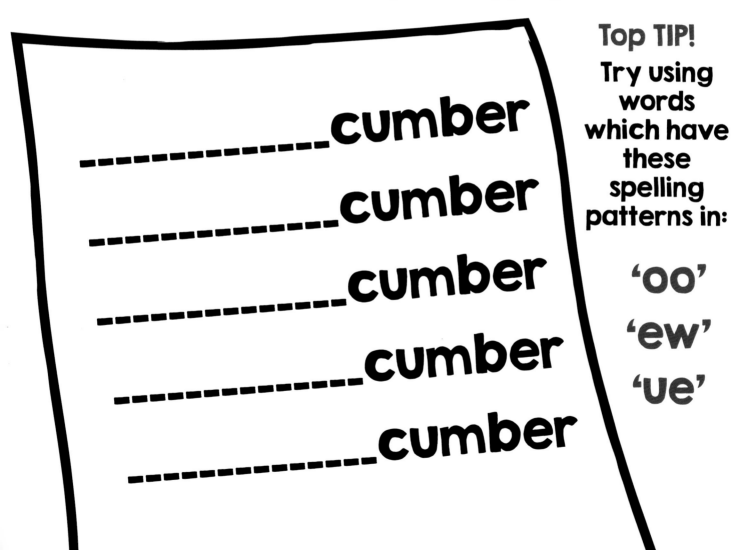

_____cumber

_____cumber

_____cumber

_____cumber

_____cumber

Top TIP!

Try using words which have these spelling patterns in:

'oo'

'ew'

'ue'

Doodles!

Follow these instructions to draw your own cucumber!

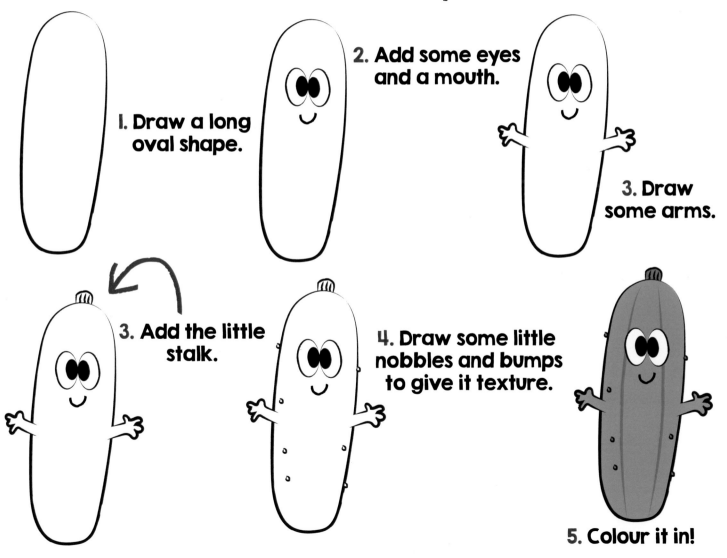

1. Draw a long oval shape.

2. Add some eyes and a mouth.

3. Draw some arms.

3. Add the little stalk.

4. Draw some little nobbles and bumps to give it texture.

5. Colour it in!

Doodles!

Here's some space to try out your own doodles. When you've drawn a regular cucumber, try and draw some of your own ideas!

About the Author

Kev Payne

Kev is an author, illustrator, poet and former primary school teacher. He was inspired to become a writer through his own teachers at school who gave him a real love of learning, reading and writing.

After teaching for 17 years, Kev now spends his time writing stories and poetry, illustrating books and playing the ukulele - sometimes all at the same time. (Unsuccessfully)

He also regularly visits schools to try and encourage and inspire children with their own writing and drawing.

Find out more about Kev here:
www.andonart.co.uk

 andonart hugsfromdad andonart

Also Available

Isbn 978-1916408807

SOCK IT TO ME!

Have you ever covered a baby in ketchup? Have you had to sit on the naughty step? Have you got a magic bike? Have you ever swallowed a fly?! Poet, illustrator and teacher, Kev Payne, has. Join him as he presents a collection of over 50 poems about sausages, school, science, balloons, long car journeys and exactly what teachers are thinking when they are stood up at the front.

"A laugh-out-loud extravaganza of poetry for children!"
Dan Metcalf, Author of Codebusters, The Lottie Lipton Adventures, Jamie Jones and Dino Wars.

'B' IS FOR BLOBFISH

Think you know your A, B, C?
Take a unique journey around the animal kingdom meeting creatures that are often overlooked and under-loved.

Which animal likes to take sand baths?

Which has a pot belly to help digest leaves?

Which creature has tentacles for a nose?

Find out the answers to these, and more, in 'B is for Blobfish'!

Isbn 978193998107

This book belo

Dazzle D
-Unicorn-

Steve
-Dinosaur-

Piggory Doo
-Dragon-

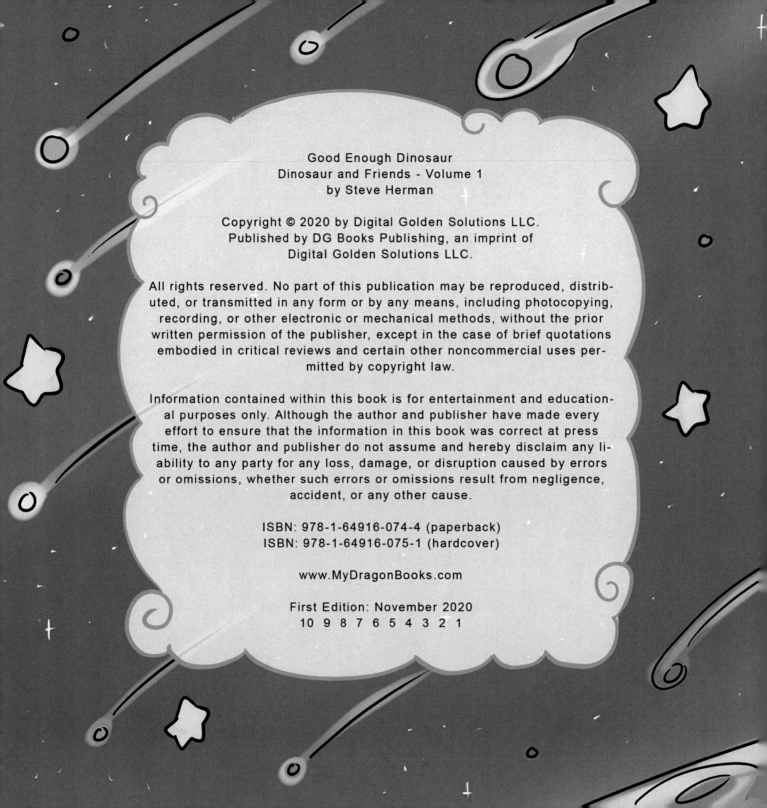

Good Enough Dinosaur
Dinosaur and Friends - Volume 1
by Steve Herman

ISBN: 978-1-64916-074-4 (paperback)
ISBN: 978-1-64916-075-1 (hardcover)

www.MyDragonBooks.com

First Edition: November 2020
10 9 8 7 6 5 4 3 2 1

GOOD ENOUGH
DINOSAUR
Dinosaur and Friends – Volume 1
Steve Herman

Hey, did you hear what Drew did?
He rode his bike in a big race.
He even won a trophy
For coming in first place!

And Allie baked some cookies
To celebrate his win;
Yum! They were delicious!
I hope she bakes us some again.

And Diggory Doo can make a fire
Any ole times he likes;
And Drew's an awesome superstar
When it comes to riding bikes.

Steve, you must be joking;
I can't imagine what you mean!
You're the coolest dinosaur
That we have ever seen!

Steve, you are a whiz at math—
You always figure out
How to solve the problems—
You're the best, I have no doubt!

My name is _____

I am good enough!

{Your picture here}

Made in the USA
Las Vegas, NV
25 November 2022